# SCOTT JOPLIN FAVORITES

**ARRANGED BY**
## JAMES BASTIEN

## CONTENTS

ISBN  0-8497-6087-9

Any reproduction, adaptation or arrangement of this work in whole or in part
without the consent of the copyright owner constitutes an infringement of copyright.
© 1975 General Words and Music Co., San Diego, Ca.
Inter. Copyright Secured    All Rights Reserved    Printed in U.S.A.

# SCOTT JOPLIN

The Ragtime craze swept the country during the Gay Nineties and flourished from about 1894 to 1918. A torrent of rags poured forth from numerous entertainer-composers. The acknowledged "King of Ragtime" was Scott Joplin. Because of the commercial exploitation by tin-pan alley, Ragtime finally collapsed and gave way to the Jazz Era. A revival began to stir around 1950 as Ragtime Clubs sprang up around the country. Clamor for Ragtime broke loose again in 1974 with the movie "THE STING," which featured many of Joplin's rags arranged by Marvin Hamlisch. Practically overnight "The Entertainer" became one of the top tunes on the charts and its catchy melodies were heard everywhere. Ragtime was off and running again!

The old Ragtime piano style was characterized by a bouncing, steady oom-pah bass under a colorful, syncopated melody. The melody was so syncopated, in fact, that this style music was first called "ragged time," finally, "ragtime."

Scott Joplin, a black musician thought to have been born in Texarkana, Texas, in 1868, came from a musical family. His mother sang and played the banjo, his father played the violin and his brother played the guitar. When his father bought a square grand piano, Scott taught himself how to play. By the age of eleven he became proficient enough to attract the attention of a German music teacher who gave him lessons.

When he was seventeen Joplin left home to seek his fortune in music. He moved to St. Louis where he played in the "honky-tonks" on Chestnut and Market Streets from 1885 to 1893. Joplin traveled to Chicago for the World's Columbian Exposition in 1893. He moved for a brief period to Sedalia, Missouri, where he played second cornet in the Queen City Concert Band. During the next two years he toured with a vocal group he had formed. During this period Joplin began to write down some of the compositions he performed, and subsequently some were published. His first published composition was "Original Rags" in 1899.

Joplin returned to Sedalia and attended George Smith College, a black school sponsored by the Methodist Church. While living in Sedalia he composed his famous "Maple Leaf Rag," named for the Maple Leaf Club where he was playing. Because of the popularity of the "Maple Leaf Rag," pianists from all over flocked to the Maple Leaf Club to hear Joplin play. Despite the popularity of this rag, Joplin had a difficult time getting it published. Finally a music dealer named Joseph Stark heard "Maple Leaf Rag," and published it. This piece became a nationwide success for Joplin and Stark and remained Joplin's biggest hit throughout his lifetime.

Stark moved to St. Louis and established a publishing firm and Joplin followed, bringing his bride. Joplin prospered from royalties and retired from performing ragtime music to devote his time to composing and teaching. In 1902 he produced "Ragtime Dance," a folk ballet. Shortly after this, he composed his first opera, "A Guest of Honor." Neither the ballet nor the opera was successful. At about this time, Joplin began to have personal problems. His baby daughter died when she was just a few months old. Relations with his wife became strained, and they separated.

Joplin moved back to Chicago, then to St. Louis and to New York within a year. He began to perform again and composed more rags, hoping to recoup from his failures in ballet and opera. After the death of his first wife, he remarried in 1909 and settled in a house on West 41st Street in New York. Later he moved uptown to Harlem, and there he began to work on another opera, "Treemonisha." This opera received a disappointing performance in Harlem in 1915. As a result, the disaster weakened Joplin's spirit severely. His health worsened, and he was taken to Manhattan State Hospital in the Fall of 1916. He deteriorated and finally died on April 1, 1917, only forty-nine years old.

Fortunately, a legacy of bright, happy music remains from this great American composer. Joplin produced a wealth of rags; his style ranged from up-beat marches to stunning serenades. Joplin's rags were written in disciplined forms which had astonishing variety and subtlety. Usually the rag had four 16-measure themes strung together like a rondo, constantly reprising the first theme after each succeeding theme. Scott Joplin published 39 piano rags, some of the most popular being:

Maple Leaf Rag (1899)
Peacherine Rag (1901)
The Entertainer (1902)
Fig Leaf Rag (1908)
Wall Street Rag (1909)
Stoptime Rag (1910)
Scott Joplin's New Rag (1912)
Magnetic Rag (1914)
Bethena - A Concert Waltz (1915)
Ragtime Dance (1916)

For an in-depth study of Ragtime music and its composers, see: "THEY ALL PLAYED RAGTIME," Revised Edition, by Rudi Blesh and Harriet Janis (New York: Quick Fox, Inc., 1966).

# THE ENTERTAINER

## Simplified Version

SCOTT JOPLIN
Arranged by James Bastien

Any reproduction, adaptation or arrangement of this work in whole or in part
without the consent of the copyright owner constitutes an infringement of copyright.
© 1975 General Words and Music Co., San Diego, Ca.
Inter. Copyright Secured    All Rights Reserved    Printed in U.S.A.

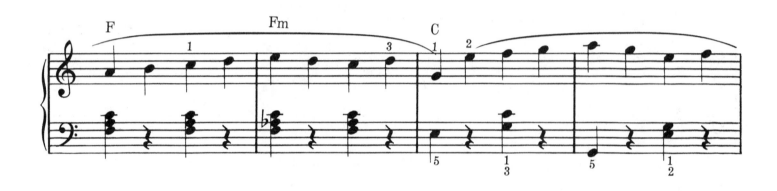

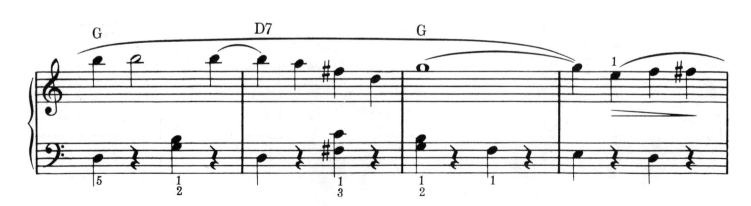

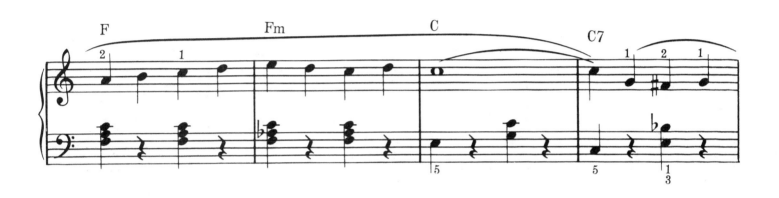

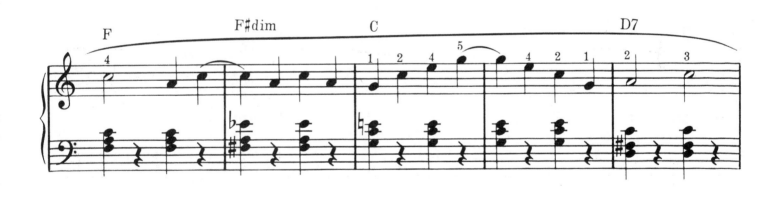

# RAGTIME DANCE

**Simplified Version**

SCOTT JOPLIN
Arranged by James Bastien

Any reproduction, adaptation or arrangement of this work in whole or in part
without the consent of the copyright owner constitutes an infringement of copyright.
© 1975 General Words and Music Co., San Diego, Ca.
Inter. Copyright Secured    All Rights Reserved    Printed in U.S.A.

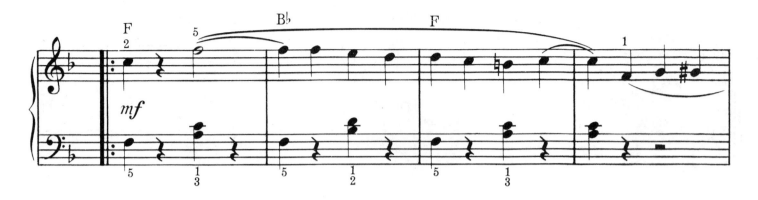

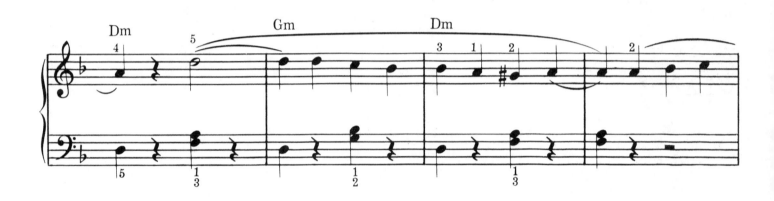

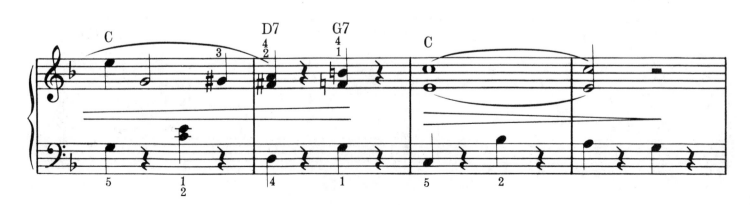

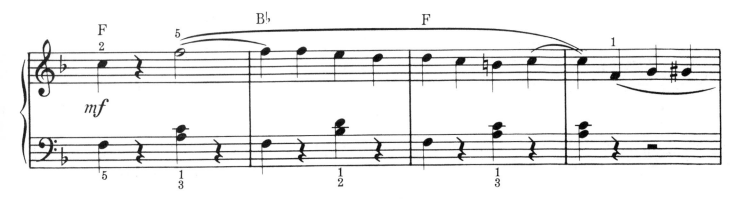

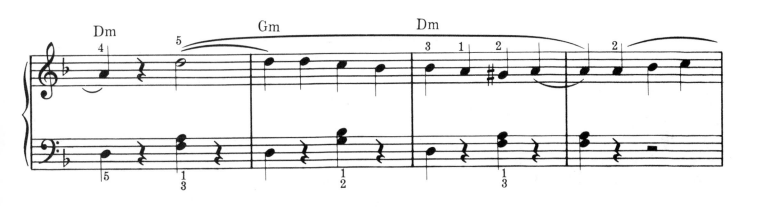

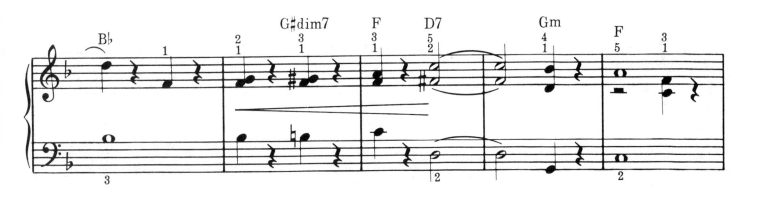

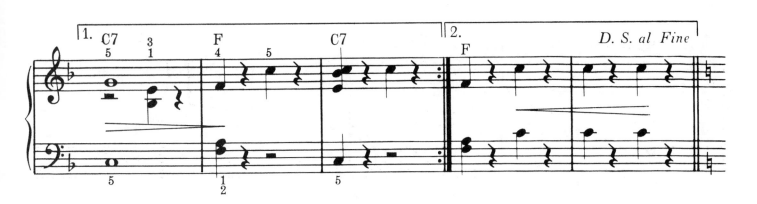

GP90

# MAPLE LEAF RAG

## Simplified Version

SCOTT JOPLIN
Arranged by James Bastien

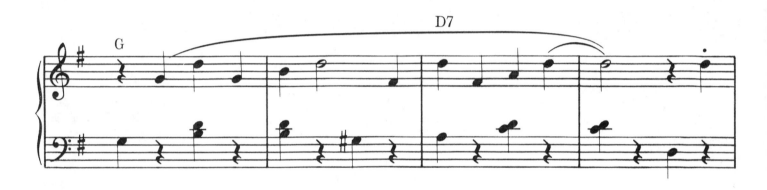

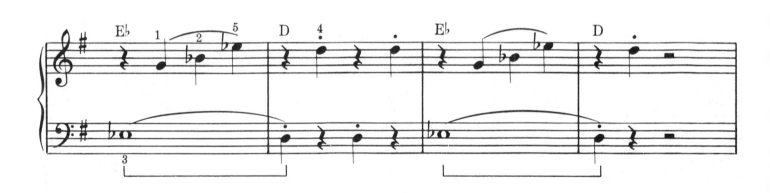

Any reproduction, adaptation or arrangement of this work in whole or in part
without the consent of the copyright owner constitutes an infringement of copyright.
© 1975 General Words and Music Co., San Diego, Ca.
Inter. Copyright Secured    All Rights Reserved    Printed in U.S.A.

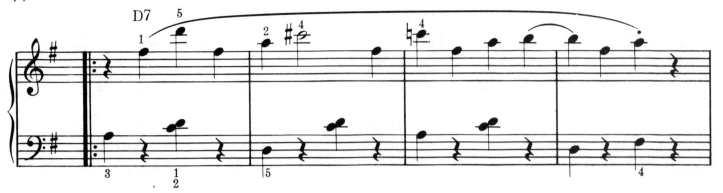

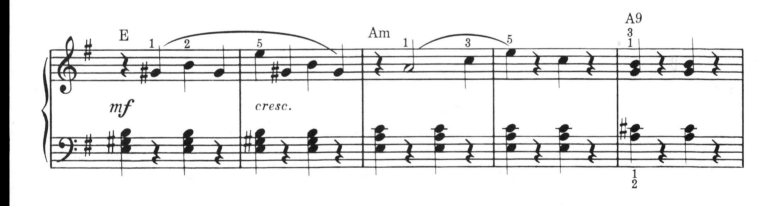

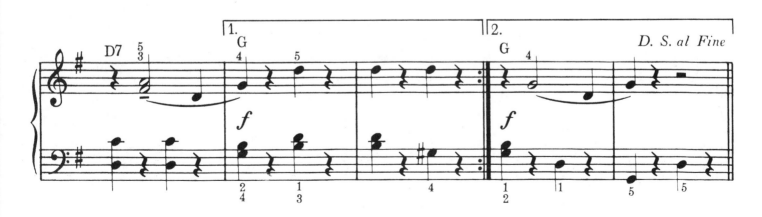

GP 90

# BETHENA
# A Concert Waltz
## Simplified Version

SCOTT JOPLIN
Arranged by James Bastien

Valse tempo

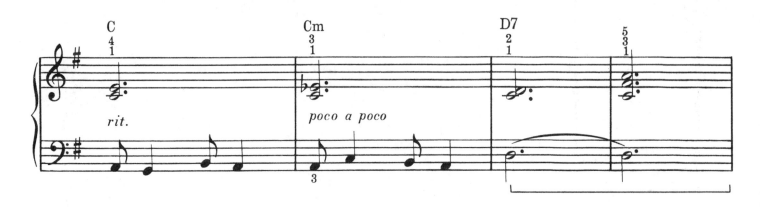

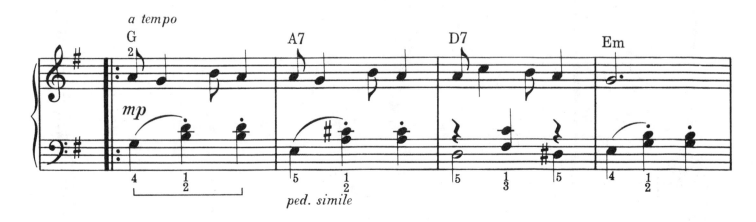

Any reproduction, adaptation or arrangement of this work in whole or in part
without the consent of the copyright owner constitutes an infringement of copyright.
© 1975 General Words and Music Co., San Diego, Ca.
Inter. Copyright Secured    All Rights Reserved    Printed in U.S.A.